this book is dedicated to spider-man and
batman for their smart outfits.
(sorry, superman, yours is a bit of a laugh.)

b. wing : mais quel talent !
c'est en voyant son book que
j'ai décidé de montrer à Hong Kong
ses merveilleuses sculptures
elles m'ont semblé si touchantes
et drôles en même temps...
j'aime aussi beaucoup ses dessins

'She's evil.
I just met her briefly a few times in some casual
gatherings, but I've never stopped planning secretly
for some collaboration with her since I saw her and
her works for the first time.
Her stuff is simple in form, but deep in meaning. It's
like a hybrid of Calvin & Hobbes stories and Tim
Burton's tragedies, with a touch of Snoopy's sunny
and bright attitude.
b.wing, I'll be after you. Watch out!'

– Chet Lam Yat-fung, songwriter

'M. LAU – THE FIRST LOOK
IF YOU WANT TO BE PERFECT,
YOU'VE COME TO THE WRONG PLACE.
"i will hate you till i die"'

– Michael Lau, artist

'I've known b.wing since our collaboration on the custom toy last winter, but I know her art much longer than that. I like the simple way she creates her style. A very outstanding artist.'

– Raymond Choy, President of Toy2R

'The flow of lines, the vibration of colours, the construction of space... People would find all these elements in pictures. However, to all genuine artists, passions and emotions that penetrate into their pictures are what they pursue. I feel the intense passions and emotions through b.wing's artwork. In the years to come, her artistry may be refined, her style may be polished, but these are comparatively insignificant, for b.wing has already reached the goal.'

– Zunzi (尊子), local cartoonist and artist

'Les cheveux de B' – Rolitoland secret place n° 105

– Rolitoboy, French artist

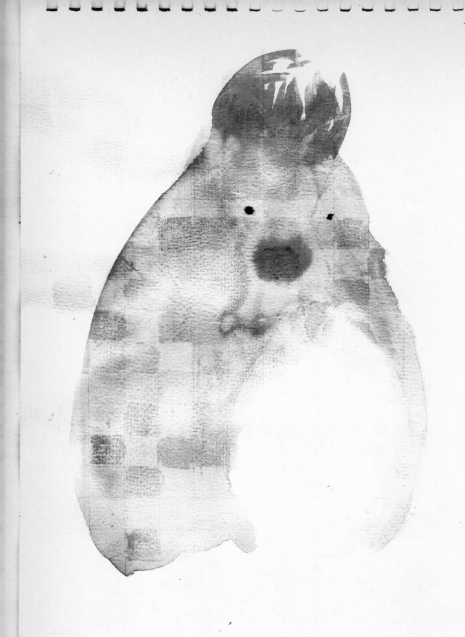

Thanks to my editor, Ling C, the Marketing Department, Siddal and Doris, and the staff of SCMP Books for their invaluable help.

Many thanks to Mme Agnes b (and all her devoted co-workers), Chet Lam Yat-fung, Michael Lau, Raymond Choy, Rolitoboy and Zunzi for their kind support, their sense of humour, their creative mind, their passion, and their capability of getting things done beautifully. Hat down and two thumbs up!

Thanks to my family, TPAC, AMJ and CYB.

My thanks also go to Anego B, Anissa K, Bil T, Ed Y, Florance Y, Helen C, Jose, KGG, Laurent G, Mavis L, Rebecca Reinhart, Selina, Stephen C, Theo T and TTM.

Special thanks to Cary, Dominique and Dickson.

Thank you all for putting up with my multiple personalities and anti-social behaviour.
I enjoy every minute of it though…

IF YOU DO
TO BE PEF
YOU'VE CO
RIGHT PL

TWANT

ECT

IE TO THE

CE

can you tell me who i am?

mum said it's terrible to go through life
while wishing you were someone else.

being a rabbit is only my part-time job.

every time when i turn my back to my mum...

I will

I w.

i can't remember the things i wish to forget.

i'm pessimistic and i like French fries.

i haven't got enough sleep since Christmas...

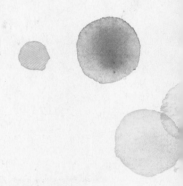

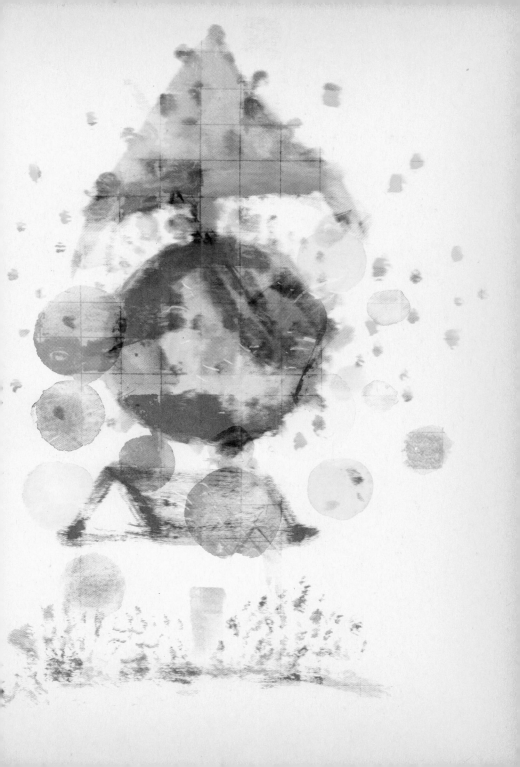

i trod in a circle and made a thousand fingerprints on my fringe.

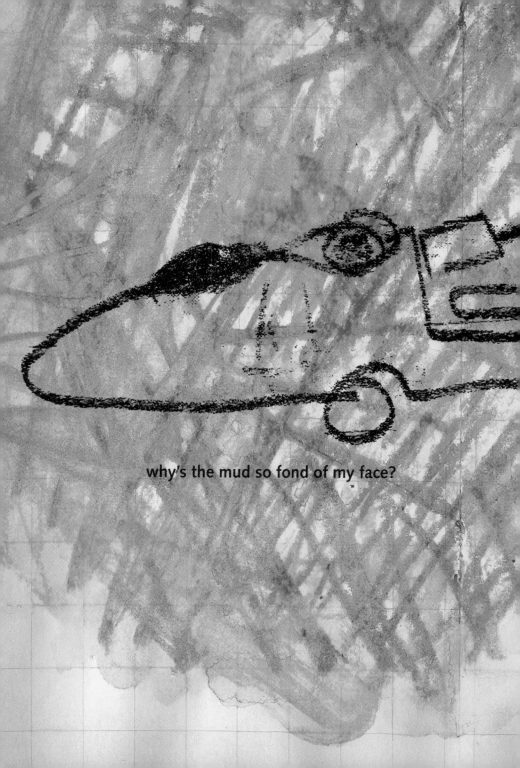

why's the mud so fond of my face?

when i let my hair grow...

i'm very anti-social in a traffic jam.

Dearest B

How are you? I am v

I keep reading your letter over
happier I Miss you
99% of the time, t
is spent sleeping while

I Love you, a
you? And try to
and we will forget

See you

Happy

ressed today because I am so lonley

er again because it makes me feel

mer 1% of the time
e.

ver forget that will
mber the good times
d okay.

y dreams
smilling.

A

I swear I don't know where it's gone

the day i dyed my hair pink.

how come i get fed up every night?

if you're depressed, i'll cheer you up, hopefully.

are there any side-effects of being so trendy?

i'm sorry, Mickey. yes... i love someone else.

the worst memoir of a geisha in the 80s.

even Rei asks why in the morning.

Do i look elegant
to you, Mr Armani?

anyone who believes in psychokinesis, raise your...

i've forgotten where i left my hook.

is your hair still short? do your cheeks still shine?

Phone Me M

Please .

i'd like to cry now. is that alright with you?

sometimes i feel like i'm living in a circus.

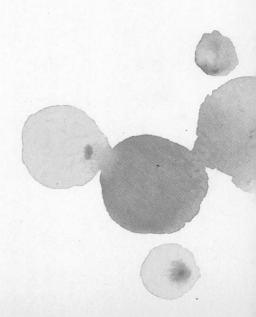

'a bad hair night, eh?' the mouse said.

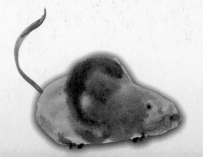

'you look nice today,' the mouse said.

can anyone get me out of here?

Dearest A

Are there any books where all the
stupids get eaten by
monsters on the first page?

yours B

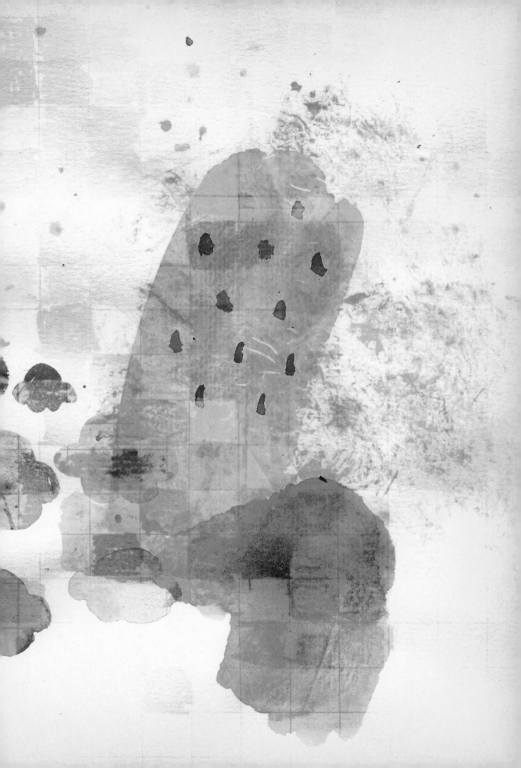

'B' is always at my back.

i'm having a break. do you mind taking photos with Mickey first?

A B C D E F G H I J K L M N
N O P Q R S T U V W X Y Z
A B C D E F G H I J K L M N

I will love yo

will you come on a cloudless day...

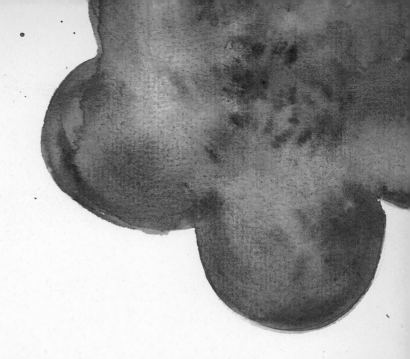

and bring me some chocolate cake?

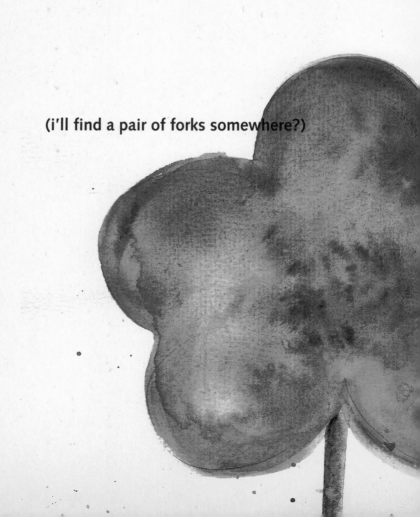

(i'll find a pair of forks somewhere?)

are you still sleeping in the
    same bed with that little pink
doll hanging?

If you don't want to be perfect, you've come to the right place
'I will love you till you die'
by b.wing
© SCMP Book Publishing Limited

ISBN-10: 962-17-9137-5
ISBN-13: 978-962-17-9137-5

First Published June 2006

Cover design by b.wing and Mak Wai Lung
Layout design by b.wing and Mak Wai Lung
Edited by Cheung Pui Ling

SCMP Book Publishing Limited
15th Floor, Somerset House
Taikoo Place, 979 King's Road
Quarry Bay, Hong Kong

Tel: (852) 2565 2545
Website: www.scmpbooks.com
Printed and published in Hong Kong